TREASURY OF TERROR!

- The long-lost *first* exploit of Count Dracula!
- An eerie mission from the far future to a world in peril!
- Revenge that lived beyond the grave!

MASTERS OF TERROR!

Lovecraft, Derleth, Bloch, Kipling, Bierce, Bram Stoker—their famous stories of supernatural horror presented in pictorial form by the best of today's action artists!

MR. TERROR!

Selected by Christopher Lee—the movies' most sensational portrayer of arch-fiends such as Dr. Fu Manchu, Dracula, Rasputin, and Frankenstein's Monster!

Christopher Lee's

TREASURY OF TERROR

Stories by

H. P. Lovecraft and August Derleth,
Robert Bloch, Rudyard Kipling,
Ambrose Bierce, Bram Stoker

PYRAMID BOOKS ▲ NEW YORK

ACKNOWLEDGMENTS

"Wentworth's Day" by H. P. Lovecraft and August Derleth. Copyright 1957 by August Derleth; adapted by permission of the author and the author's agent, Scott Meredith Literary Agency, Inc.

"The Past Master" by Robert Bloch. Copyright by The McCall Corporation for *Blue Book;* adapted by permission of the author and the author's agent, Harry Altshuler.

The publishers wish to express their appreciation to Mr. Haywood Norton who made available a rare edition of "Dracula's Guest" to the adapters of this story.

Christopher Lee's **TREASURY OF TERROR**

A PYRAMID BOOK

First printing September, 1966

Printed in the United States of America

PYRAMID BOOKS are published by Pyramid Publications, Inc.,
444 Madison Avenue, New York, New York 10022, U.S.A.

INTRODUCTION

EVERY ONE OF US harbors within us a streak buried fathoms deep, below the apparently placid normality of our everyday appearance—a streak of rapt fascination for the Prince of Darkness and all his works. There is beyond doubt an innate attraction and appeal that has lasted through generations, for the works of the masters of twilight lore.

All of us thrill to escape from the seemingly humdrum world of the familiar and the known to the unseen world of the macabre. It is no coincidence that the word "macabre" itself derives from the Arabic—*Ma Kabr*, "from the grave."

Learned psychologists, psychiatrists and other talented members of the medical profession are apt to pronounce in weighty terms upon the healing properties of "a good shock." As in certain forms of treatment, i.e., electrotherapy, a shock or sudden jolt to the system can produce curative results.

I have been asked more times than I care to remember whether I feel there is any harm in the fictionalized representations of the gruesome and the grotesque. I have always replied that, in my own personal opinion, there can never be any form of deleterious effect on the minds and souls of the many millions who create for themselves a welcome escape into unreality—when they ally themselves instinctively with the forces of good they see arrayed before them in the constant and unrelenting battle against the Dark Ones. There, but for the grace of God . . .

There is also no doubt in my mind whatsoever that the literature of this subject, either in books or transferred into the realms of the living theatre and cinema, can never be harmful in any degree, except to those poor souls who already suffer, through no fault of their own, from twisted and unbalanced minds. I feel certain that the shock element inherent in these great legends is a salutary one. Like all basic emotions, those of fear, terror, horror, inevitably form a type of safety valve which releases pent-up tensions and repressions through the medium of an individual reaction.

To this extent I refute utterly the suggestion, often and mistakenly quoted, that there is a pernicious effect on the imaginations of the young and impressionable. Fear is a basic human emotion like laughter and tears and happiness. And strange though it may seem, there is no doubt at all that the reactions of the reader or audience are pleasurable. We have all experienced at one time or another a delicious chill of apprehension.

The collection of stories included in this book could well comprise what, for lack of a better word, I will term Lycanthropicvampiristicscientificomnibus. They are five, and they comprise a choice selection from the works of the greatest exponents, both classical and modern, of the unknown.

With "The Past Master" of Robert Bloch, we find ourselves enmeshed in scientific fantasy which may one day indeed become reality. We all know what can so easily develop from "a trivial incident."

Rudyard Kipling's "The Mark of the Beast" couples the age-old savagery of the East with unnameable suggestions of the power of evil. And this from the pen of a man known mainly to the world for his renowned skill in recounting stories of Imperial Derring-Do.

The "secret black and midnight chill" of "Dracula's Guest" shows the work of Bram Stoker at its immortal best. It is perhaps not generally known, but this particular story originally formed part of the great masterpiece *Dracula* but was excised by the author.

Ambrose Bierce, who penned the fey intellectualism of "The Death of Halpin Frayser," himself provided a mystery no less strange than any of his stories. He disappeared from mortel ken in Mexico in 1914, at the age of 70, and was never seen again. Today, he would be 122 years of age. It would therefore be typical of the man if he were still alive, a fitting footnote to his life and works.

And finally, we are enchanted by the whirling mists of H.P. Lovecraft's unmentionable world, with its horrendous song of the whippoorwills, all set amidst the lurking trolls of witch-haunted Arkhan. The immortal creator of the mighty Cthulhu Mythos has written nothing more eery than "Wentworth's Day."

This is a world of black ice and towering decay. The inhabitants of this world, as you read these stories, will throng about you, chittering and ululating, as they touch the innermost recesses of your sanity.

And remember this: I wish them well.

CHRISTOPHER LEE

THE MARK OF THE BEAST

RUDYARD KIPLING

Adapter: CRAIG TENNIS

Artist: JOHNNY CRAIG

The MARK of the BEAST!
by Rudyard Kipling
Your Gods and my Gods ... do you or I know which are the stronger?
NATIVE PROVERB

EAST OF SUEZ, SOME HOLD, MAN IS HANDED OVER TO THE POWER OF THE GODS AND DEVILS OF ASIA...AND IF THIS THEORY BE TRUE, IT ACCOUNTS FOR SOME OF THE MORE UNNECESSARY HORRORS OF MY LIFE IN INDIA...

WELL, FLEETE, WELCOME TO OUR WHITE ISLAND.
THANK YOU, STRICKLAND. IT'S AN HONOR TO BE A GUEST IN YOUR HOME.
I'M GETTING USED TO RIDING FIFTEEN MILES TO DINNER EVEN IF IT MEANS RISKING A KHYBEREE BULLET WHERE MY DRINK SHOULD BE!

SOME OF US WERE TO GO ON TO BURMA AND SOME TO THE SOUDAN, SOME TO FIND STARS AND SOME TO FIND MEDALS AND WE ALL STROVE TO MAKE MONEY ON INSUFFICIENT EXPERIENCE.
SHOULD AULD ACQAINTANCE BE FORGOT
POLO
CHAMPION
MORE SHERRY AND BITTERS NOW, CHAMPAGNE TIL DESSERT, THEN CAPRI, BENEDICTINE WITH COFFEE, WHISKEY AND SODA WITH POOL, AND BRANDY AT HALF PAST TWO...

AFTER TRYING TO LEAP-FROG INTO THE SADDLE...
STOP THAT COUGHING, YOU FOOL ANIMAL!
...THE HORSE BROKE AND WENT HOME.
SO WE FORMED A GUARD OF DISHONOR TO TAKE FLEETE HOME...
WHAT TEMPLE'S THAT?
HANUMAN, THE MONKEY GOD. I'M KIND TO HIS PEOPLE, THE GREAT GRAY APES. ONE NEVER KNOWS WHEN HE'LL NEED A FRIEND.

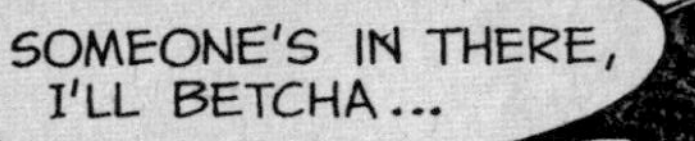

WE COULD HEAR THE VOICES OF MEN CHANTING HYMNS...
SOMEONE'S IN THERE, I'LL BETCHA...

DON'T LET HIM GO IN!
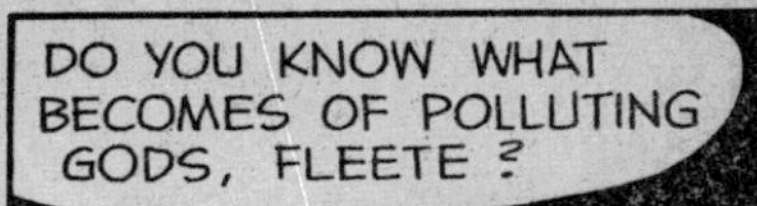

DO YOU KNOW WHAT BECOMES OF POLLUTING GODS, FLEETE?

SEE THAT? MARK OF THE B-BEASHT! I MADE IT. ISHN'T IT FINE?... GOOD OL' HANUMAN, HE'S A FINE PILLOW...

THE LEPER MOVED CLOSER TO FLEETE...

FLEETE WAS STILL GORGEOUSLY DRUNK.

FLEETE BEGAN VIOLENT SHIVERING FITS AND SWEATING...
I HATE THE SMELL OF THE BAZAAR! WHY ARE SLAUGHTER HOUSES PERMITTED HERE? CAN'T YOU SMELL THE BLOOD?

WE FINALLY GOT FLEETE TO BED...
DID YOU SEE FLEETE SCRATCHING HIS BREAST AS HE FELL ASLEEP?
...I DON'T UNDERSTAND WHY THEY DIDN'T KILL US AT THE TEMPLE... STRANGE...

IN THE MORNING, FLEETE SEEMED UNWELL.

QUEER MOSQUITOS YOU HAVE IN THESE PARTS. I'VE BEEN BITTEN TO PIECES! THEY WERE PINK THIS MORNING, NOW THEY'VE GROWN BLACK! BY JOVE! WHAT IS IT?

WE COULDN'T ANSWER HIM...

AFTER BREAKFAST WE DECIDED TO GO OUT FOR A RIDE, BUT THE HORSES SCREAMED AND LATHERED...
WHAT'S THE MATTER WITH THEM?
THEY DON'T SEEM TO LOVE YOU, FLEETE.
NONSENSE! MY MARE WILL FOLLOW ME LIKE A DOG.
BUT SHE PLUNGED, KNOCKED HIM DOWN, AND BROKE AWAY.

INSTEAD OF CHASING HIS PROPERTY...
I'M SLEEPY. I'M GOING BACK TO BED.
NOTICE HIS PECULIAR MANNER. THE WAY HE ATE LIKE A BEAST...
AND THE MARKS ON HIS BREAST...
I CAN'T TELL YOU WHAT I THINK, BECAUSE YOU'D CALL ME A MADMAN. STAY AND WATCH IF YOU WILL, BUT DON'T TELL ME WHAT YOU THINK TILL I'VE MADE UP MY MIND.

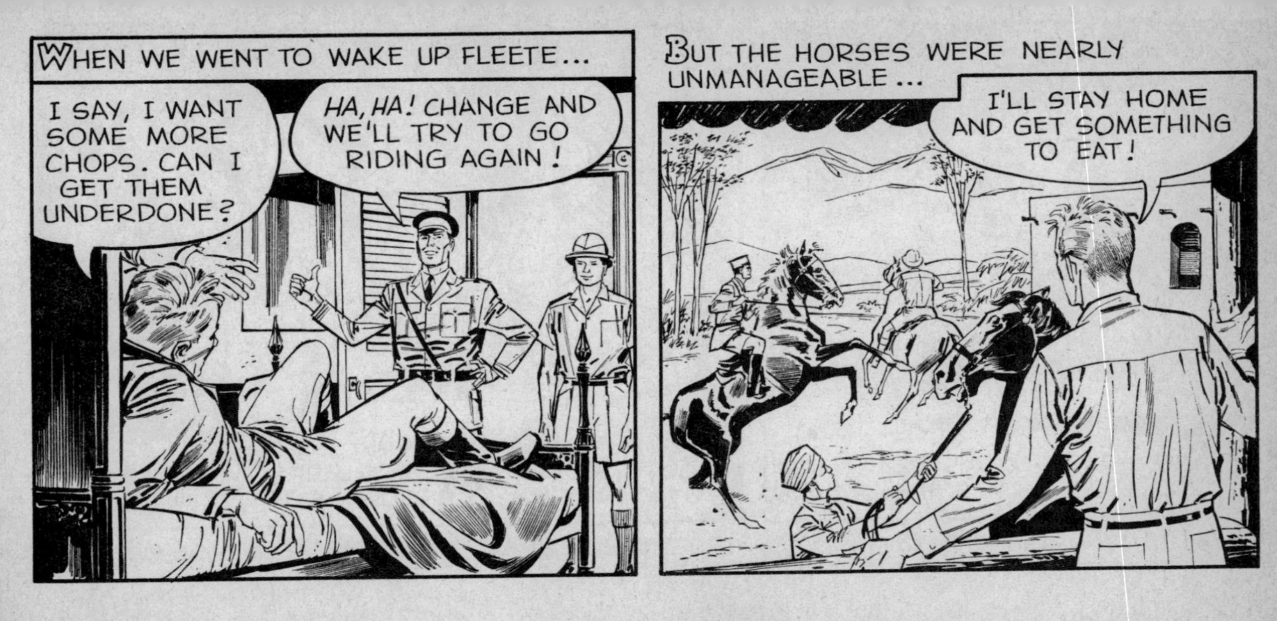
WHEN WE WENT TO WAKE UP FLEETE...
I SAY, I WANT SOME MORE CHOPS. CAN I GET THEM UNDERDONE?
HA, HA! CHANGE AND WE'LL TRY TO GO RIDING AGAIN!
BUT THE HORSES WERE NEARLY UNMANAGEABLE...
I'LL STAY HOME AND GET SOMETHING TO EAT!

AS WE PASSED THE TEMPLE, THE LEPER APPEARED...
MEWW... MEWW!
HE'S NOT ONE OF THE REGULAR PRIESTS. I THINK I'D LIKE TO LAY MY HANDS ON HIM.
RETURNING AT SEVEN THAT NIGHT... 
CARELESS RUFFIANS MY SERVANTS ARE! THERE'S NOT A LIGHT ON!

WHAT ARE YOU DOING, GROVELING ABOUT?
WHAT THE DEVIL'S WRONG WITH YOU?
I'VE BEEN... GARDENING... I THINK I'M GOING FOR A LONG WALK... ALL NIGHT.
THERE WAS SOMETHING EXCESSIVELY OUT OF ORDER.
HERE, FLEETE, GET UP. WE'LL GET THE LAMPS AND HAVE DINNER!
NO LAMPS! IT'S MUCH NICER LIKE THIS. LET'S HAVE CHOPS... BLOODY ONES WITH GRISTLE!

THERE'S GOING TO BE BIG TROUBLE TONIGHT!
I'LL HELP YOU KEEP HIM IN. NORTHERN INDIA'S BITTERLY COLD IN DECEMBER.
WE HAD GOTTEN HIM IN THE BUNGALOW WHEN THE NOISE OUTSIDE BEGAN...
HE'S MAKING BEAST NOISES!
LIKE A WOLF!
GRRROWWW
GRRR
OWWEWUUUUU

WE GAGGED FLEETE AND BOUND HIM WITH LEATHER THONGS...

GO GET DOCTOR DUMOISE, AT ONCE!

NO GOOD, THIS ISN'T DOCTOR'S WORK!

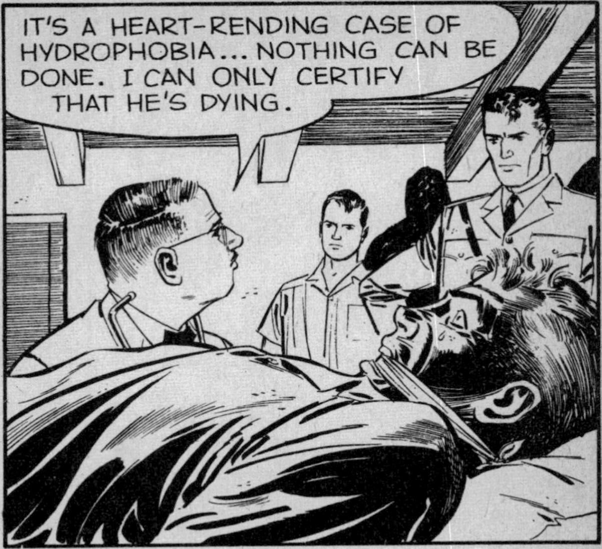

IT'S A HEART-RENDING CASE OF HYDROPHOBIA... NOTHING CAN BE DONE. I CAN ONLY CERTIFY THAT HE'S DYING.

AFTER DUMOISE LEFT, STRICKLAND WHISPERED HIS SUSPICIONS TO ME...
RIDICULOUS! EVEN IF THE LEPER BEWITCHED FLEETE FOR POLLUTING THE IMAGE OF HANUMAN, THE PUNISHMENT COULD NOT HAVE FALLEN SO QUICKLY!
BUT IT SOON APPEARED THAT HE WAS RIGHT...
LOOK AT HIM SUFFER! IF HE'S CALLED AGAIN I SHALL TAKE THE LAW INTO MY OWN HANDS, AND I'LL ORDER YOU TO HELP ME!
HOWWEWWWW

STRICKLAND GOT THE BARREL OF AN OLD SHOTGUN, SOME WIRE FISHING LINE, CORD, A SHEET AND GLOVES...

WE PREPARED TO CAPTURE THE HOWLING CREATURE OUTSIDE...

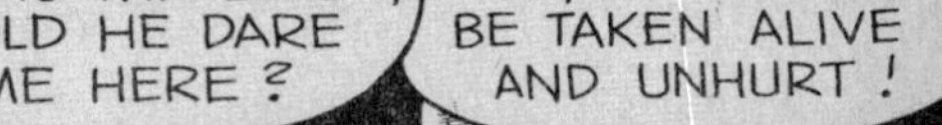

HE'S EVIDENTLY MOVING AROUND THE HOUSE AS REGULARLY AS A NIGHT-WATCHMAN. WE'LL GO OUT THE WINDOW AND JUMP HIM IN THE BUSHES!
OOWUUEEEE
THE LEPER WAS DANCING WITH HIS SHADOW IN THE MOONLIGHT!

HE'S STRONGER THAN I THOUGHT HE'D BE !

NOW WE'LL HAVE HIM CURE THIS CASE !
AHHHOWW!

THE REST SHOULD NOT BE TOLD.

THE DAWN WAS BREAKING BEFORE THE LEPER SPOKE.

MEEEMMEWW...

STOP WHINING AND TAKE AWAY THE SPIRIT!

WE BADE THE LEPER GO, AND GAVE HIM EVERY-THING THAT HAD TOUCHED HIS UNCLEAN BODY.

TWENTY-FOUR HOURS! ENOUGH TO ASSURE MY DISMISSAL FROM THE POLICE FORCE, BESIDES PERMANENT QUARTERS IN A LUNATIC ASYLUM! ARE WE AWAKE?
THERE'S THE GUN BARREL... AND THE SMELL IS ALL TOO REAL!
THE BLACK LEOPARD-ROSETTE ON YOUR CHEST HAS DISAPPEARED!
CONFOUND YOU FELLOWS! HAPPY NEW YEAR! NEVER MIX YOUR LIQUORS! I'M NEARLY DEAD!
THANKS, BUT YOU'RE OVER-DUE. TODAY'S THE SECOND.

DUMOISE HAD RETURNED TO SIGN THE DEATH CERTIFICATE...

WHAT DO YOU THINK, FRIEND?
"THERE ARE MORE THINGS..."
HORRID DOGGY SMELL HERE. YOU SHOULD REALLY KEEP YOUR TERRIERS IN BETTER ORDER, STRICK.
IT'S TERRIBLE TO SEE STRONG MEN TAKEN OVER IN HYSTERIA...
YOU'VE BOTH GONE MAD!
HAA HAA HAA!
HOOHOO HAW!
BUT BOTH OF US HAD FOUGHT FOR FLEETE'S SOUL AND DISGRACED OURSELVES AS ENGLISHMEN FOREVER.

WE NEVER TOLD FLEETE. AND SOME YEARS LATER WE DISCUSSED THE INCIDENT DISPASSIONATELY. STRICKLAND SUGGESTED I PUT IT BEFORE THE PUBLIC...

BUT IT DOES NOT CLEAR UP THE MYSTERY, FOR NO ONE BELIEVES AN UNPLEASANT STORY, AND IT IS WELL KNOWN THAT HEATHEN GODS ARE BUT BRASS AND STONE, AND TO DEAL WITH THEM IS TO BE JUSTLY CONDEMNED.

The End

WENTWORTH'S DAY

H. P. LOVECRAFT and
AUGUST DERLETH

Adapter: RUSS JONES

Artist: RUSS JONES

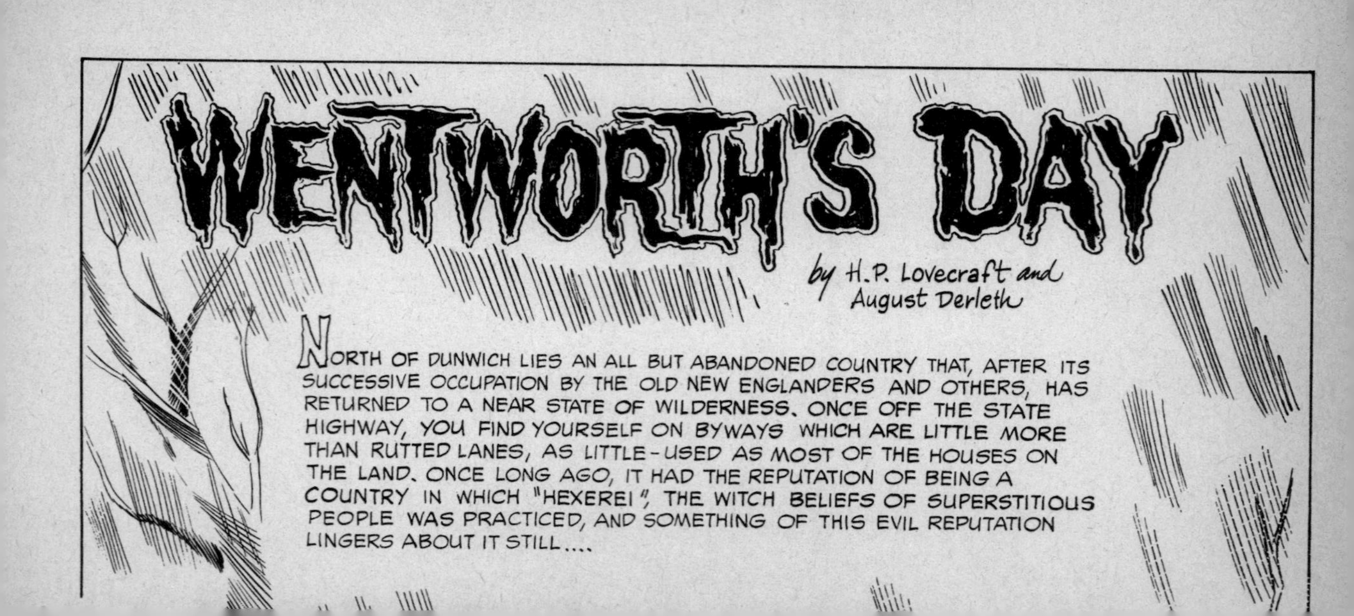
WENTWORTH'S DAY
by H.P. Lovecraft and
August Derleth
NORTH OF DUNWICH LIES AN ALL BUT ABANDONED COUNTRY THAT, AFTER ITS SUCCESSIVE OCCUPATION BY THE OLD NEW ENGLANDERS AND OTHERS, HAS RETURNED TO A NEAR STATE OF WILDERNESS. ONCE OFF THE STATE HIGHWAY, YOU FIND YOURSELF ON BYWAYS WHICH ARE LITTLE MORE THAN RUTTED LANES, AS LITTLE-USED AS MOST OF THE HOUSES ON THE LAND. ONCE LONG AGO, IT HAD THE REPUTATION OF BEING A COUNTRY IN WHICH "HEXEREI", THE WITCH BELIEFS OF SUPERSTITIOUS PEOPLE WAS PRACTICED, AND SOMETHING OF THIS EVIL REPUTATION LINGERS ABOUT IT STILL....

I HAD MADE MY LAST TRIP INTO THE VALLEY, ON MY WAY FROM DELIVERING A STOVE NOT FAR FROM DUNWICH. ALL WOULD HAVE BEEN WELL, HAD IT NOT BEEN FOR TWO UNFORESEEN FACTORS. THE RAIN, WHICH HAD BEEN HANGING IN THE HEAVENS ALL THAT DAY, FINALLY CAME DOWN IN A TORRENT...

I TURNED OFF THE HIGHWAY WITH MISGIVINGS. IF ONLY I HAD FOLLOWED MY IMPULSES TO RETURN TO DUNWICH AND TAKE ANOTHER ROAD, I MIGHT BE FREE OF THE ACCURSED NIGHTMARES WHICH HAVE TROUBLED MY SLEEP SINCE THAT NIGHT OF HORROR.

THE ROAD I TRAVELED WAS RAPIDLY WORSENING, AND DEEPENING PUDDLES OF WATER CAUSED MY MOTOR TO SPUTTER AND COUGH.

I KNEW IT WAS ONLY A QUESTION OF TIME BEFORE THE DOWNPOUR WOULD SEEP THROUGH THE HOOD AND STOP MY ENGINE ALTOGETHER. I BEGAN TO LOOK AROUND FOR ANY SIGN OF HABITATION, AND THUS I CAME AT LAST TO A PALE SQUARE OF LIGHT NOT FAR OFF THE ROAD, AND BY A LUCKY CHANCE. FOUND THE DRIVEWAY IN THE FADING GLOW OF MY HEADLAMPS...
AMOS STARK

I HAD EXPECTED TO SEE CATTLE AND HORSES, BUT THE BARN WORE AN AIR OF DESERTION AND THE HAY, WITH ITS AROMA OF PAST SUMMERS, MUST HAVE BEEN SEVERAL YEARS OLD.

I FOUND THE DOOR AND POUNDED ON IT.
IS ANYBODY HOME?
THEN A QUAVERING VOICE CAME FROM INSIDE.
WHO BE YE?
I'M A SALESMAN SEEKING SHELTER.

THE LIGHT BEGAN TO MOVE INSIDE AS A LAMP WAS PICKED UP FROM WHERE IT STOOD. THERE WAS THE SOUND OF BOLTS AND CHAINS BEING WITHDRAWN, AND THE DOOR OPENED.
MR. STARK?
STORM KETCHED YE, EH? COME RIGHT IN THE HOUSE AN' DRY OFF. DON'T RECKON THE RAIN'LL LAST LONG NAOW.
THIS BE WENTWORTH'S DAY. I THOUGHT YEW MIGHT BE NAHUM.
NO, SIR, MY NAME IS FRED HADLEY. I'M FROM BOSTON.

AIN'T NEVER BEEN TA BOSTON, NEVER BEEN AS FUR AS ARKHAM, EVEN. GOT MY FARM WORK TA KEEP ME TA HOME.
I HOPE YOU DON'T MIND. I TOOK THE LIBERTY OF DRIVING MY CAR INTO YOUR BARN.
THE CAOWS WON'T MIND, HA, HA, HA. WOULDN'T DRIVE ONE OF THEM NEW-FANGLED CONTRAPTIONS MYSELF, BUT YEW TAOWN PEOPLE ARE ALL ALIKE. GOTTA HEV YER AUTOMOBILES.
I DIDN'T IMAGINE I LOOKED LIKE A CITY SLICKER.
I KEN TELL A TAOWN MAN RIGHT OFF. ONCT IN A WHILE, WE GET ONE MOVIN' INTA THE DEESTRICK, BUT THEY MOVE OUT SUDDENT. GUESS THEY DAON'T LIKE IT HERE. AIN'T NEVER BEEN TA NO BIG TAOWN. AIN'T SURE I WANT TA GO.

HE RAMBLED ON IN THIS FASHION FOR SO LONG THAT I WAS ABLE TO MAKE AN INVENTORY OF AMOS STARK'S LIVING ROOM. IT WAS FILLED WITH ALL KINDS OF THINGS THAT THE ANTIQUE COLLECTORS WOULD PAY WELL TO GET THEIR HANDS ON.
DO YOU LIVE ALONE, MR. STARK?
NAOW I DO, YES. ONCT THAR WAS MOLLY AN' DEWEY. ABEL WENT OFF WHEN HE WAR A BOY, AN' ELLA DIED WITH A LUNG FEVER. I BIN ALONE FOR NIGH ONTA SEVEN YEARS.

EVEN AS HE SPOKE, I OBSERVED ABOUT HIM A WAITING, WATCHFUL AIR. HE SEEMED CONSTANTLY TO BE LISTENING FOR SOME SOUND ABOVE THE DRUMMING OF THE RAIN. THERE WAS ONLY ONE, A MOUSE GNAWING AWAY SOMEWHERE IN THE OLD HOUSE.

YE WAR ALONE ON THE ROAD?

NEVER MET A SOUL THIS SIDE OF DUNWICH. SEVENTEEN MILES, I FIGURE.

GIVE OR TAKE A HALF, (*CACKLE, CHUCKLE*). THIS BE WENTWORTH'S DAY. NAHUM WENTWORTH. YEW BEEN A SALESMAN IN THESE PARTS LONG NAOW? YEW MUSTA KNOWED NAHUM WENTWORTH?

NO, SIR, I NEVER KNEW HIM. I SELL MOSTLY IN THE TOWNS. JUST ONCE IN A WHILE IN THE COUNTRY.

MIGHT NEAR EVERYBODY KNOWED NAHUM, BUT THAR WARN'T NONE KNOWED HIM AS WELL AS I DID. SEE THAT THAR BOOK? THAT THAR'S THE SEVENTH BOOK OF MOSES— IT'S GOT A SIGHT MORE LARNIN' IN IT THAN ANY OTHER BOOK I EVER SEEN. THAT THAR IS NAHUM'S BOOK
I ASSURE YOU, I NEVER HEARD OF NAHUM WENTWORTH.
OH, THAT NAHUM WAS A QUEER ONE, ALL RIGHT! BUT MEAN, AND STINGY, TOO. DON'T SEE AS HAOW YE COULD MISS KNOWIN' HIM.

I WONDERED ABOUT MY HOST'S PREOCCUPATION, INSOFAR AS HE HAD BEEN GIVEN TO READING THE "SEVENTH BOOK OF MOSES," WHICH WAS A KIND OF BIBLE FOR THE SUPPOSED HEXES. IT PURPORTED TO OFFER ALL MANNER OF SPELLS, INCANTATIONS, AND CHARMS TO THOSE READERS WHO WERE GULLIBLE ENOUGH TO BELIEVE IN THEM.
I SEE YE LOOKIN' AT HIS BOOKS. HE SAID AS HAOW I COULD HAVE 'EM SO I TOOK 'EM. GOOD BOOKS, TOO. ONLY THAT I NEED GLASSES, I'D A READ 'EM. YEW'RE WELCOME TA LOOK AT 'EM, THOUGH.
THANK YOU. YOU WERE SPEAKING OF NAHUM WENTWORTH.

OH, THAT NAHUM! I DON'T RECKON HE'D A LENT ME ALL THAT MONEY IF HE'D A KNOWED WHAT WAS TA HAPPEN TA HIM, AN' NEVER TAKE A NOTE FER IT, NEITHER. FIVE THOUSAND IT WAS!
AN' HIM TELLIN' ME HE DIDN'T HAVE NO NEED FER NO PAPER OR ANY KIND OF A NOTE, SO THAR WARN'T NO PROOF I EVER HAD THE MONEY OFF'N HIM, NOT A'TALL, JEST THE TWO OF US KNOWIN' IT, AND HE SETTIN' A DAY FIVE YEARS AFTER FER HIM TA COME FER HIS MONEY AN' HIS DUE. FIVE YEARS.

AN' THIS IS THE DAY, THIS IS WENTWORTH'S DAY. ONLY HE CAN'T COME, BECAUSE IT WARN'T NO LESS'N TWO MONTHS AFTER THAT DAY THAT HE GOT SHOT OUT HUNTIN'.

SHOT GUN IN THE BACK O' THE HEAD, PURE ACCIDENT. O' COURSE, THAR WAS THEM THAT SAID AS HAOW I DONE IT A PURPOSE, BUT I SHOWED 'EM. DROVE TO DUNWICH AND MADE OUT MY WILL TA HIS DAUGHTER, MISS GENIE, AN' LET 'EM ALL KNOW!

AND THE LOAN?
THE TIME AIN'T UP TILL MIDNIGHT TONIGHT. AN' IT DON'T SEEM LIKE NAHUM CAN KEEP HIS 'PPOINTMENT, DOES IT? AN' A GOOD THING HE CAN'T, 'CAUSE I AIN'T GOT IT.
I DID NOT ASK HOW WENTWORTH'S DAUGHTER FARED. I WAS BEGIN-NING TO FEEL THE STRAIN OF THE DAY, AND THE DRIVE THROUGH THE DOWNPOUR.
YEW'RE LOOKIN' PEAKED, YEW TIRED?
I GUESS I AM. BUT I'LL BE GOING AS SOON AS THE STORM ABATES A LITTLE.

STARK LED ME INTO THE NEXT ROOM AND SHOWED ME TO A COUCH. ON THE WAY IN, I PICKED UP THE SEVENTH BOOK OF MOSES. HE MADE NO OBJECTION, AND LEFT ME TO MY OWN DEVICES.

OUTSIDE THE RAIN STILL CAME DOWN IN TORRENTIAL GUSTS.

I FELL TO READING THE SEVENTH BOOK OF MOSES AND FOUND TO MY AMAZEMENT THAT THE READER WAS REPEATEDLY WARNED OF HOW TERRIBLE SOME OF THE WORDS WERE. I WAS COMPELLED TO COPY SOME OF THE WORST THAT CAUGHT MY EYE.
AILA... HIMEL... ADONAIJ... AMARA... ZEBAOTH... CADAS... YESERAIJE... HERALIUS...

WONDERINGLY, I SPOKE ALOUD THESE STRANGE SYLLABLES, WHICH WERE NOTHING LESS THAN A CHANT FOR THE ASSEMBLAGE OF DEVILS OR SPIRITS, OR RAISING OF THE DEAD.
AT ELEVEN O'CLOCK, THE RAIN SEEMED TO DIMINISH. I PUT OUT THE LIGHT TO REST A LITTLE BEFORE TAKING TO THE ROAD ONCE MORE. I SOON CAUGHT MYSELF LISTENING, LIKE STARK, FOR MORE THAN THE PATTER OF RAIN.

MY HOST DID NOT SIT STILL, EVERY LITTLE WHILE HE ROSE,
AND I COULD HEAR HIM SHUFFLE FROM PLACE TO PLACE.

A HUNDRED AN' FIFTY DOLLARS A YEAR, COMES TA SEVEN FIFTY ... I FELL... ALL THEY WAS TO IT... WENT OFF QUICK-LIKE ...

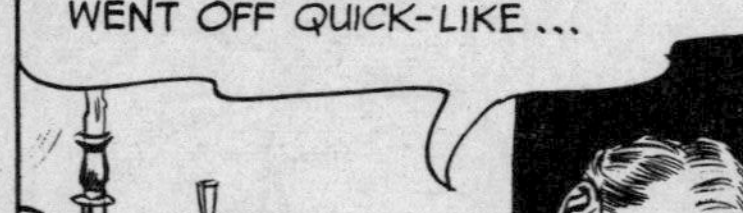
DIDN'T KNOW 'TWAS AIMED AT NAHUM.
MAYBE THE OLD MAN'S CONSCIENCE TROUBLES HIM. HE'S AS ALONE IN THE WORLD AS HE IS IN THIS HOUSE.
OUTSIDE THE WHIPPOORWILLS BEGAN TO CALL, A SIGN THAT THE SKY WAS BEGINNING TO CLEAR.
HEER THEM WHIPPOORWILLS CALLIN' FER A SOUL... CLEM WHEATLEY'S DYIN'.
THEN I DOZED OFF...

I COME NOW TO THAT PART OF MY STORY WHICH MAKES ME DOUBT MY OWN SENSES, WHICH, WHEN I LOOK BACK ON IT NOW, SEEMS IMPOSSIBLE. INDEED, MANY TIMES NOW, I WONDER WHETHER I DID NOT DREAM IT ALL — YET I KNOW IT WAS NOT A DREAM. I STILL HAVE CORROBORATING NEWSPAPER CLIPPINGS -- ABOUT AMOS STARK, ABOUT A HELLISH MOLESTATION OF A GRAVE HALF FORGOTTEN ON A HILLSIDE IN THAT ACCURSED VALLEY.
I HAD NOT BEEN DOZING LONG, WHEN I AWOKE. THE RAIN HAD CEASED, BUT THE VOICED OF THE WHIPPOORWILLS HAD MOVED CLOSER TO THE HOUSE, AND WERE IN THUNDEROUS CHORUS...
GOT TO GET ON THE ROAD... GLAD THE BIRDS WOKE ME.
BUT JUST AS I SWUNG MY FEET TO THE FLOOR, A KNOCK FELL UPON THE OUTER DOOR...
WHO BE YE?

THE KNOCK CAME AGAIN, MORE PEREMPTORILY THIS TIME. THEN I HEARD STARK'S EXCLAMATION OF TRIUMPH.
PAST MIDNIGHT!

HIS CLOCK IS TEN MINUTES FAST.

AMOS STARK WENT TO ANSWER THE DOOR. THE DOOR OPENED.

NO! NO! GO BACK! I AIN'T GOT IT— AIN'T GOT IT, I TELL YOU, GO BACK!

I HEARD HIM FALL, AND ALMOST IMMEDIATELY AFTER THERE CAME A HORRIBLE, CHOKING CRY, A SOUND OF LABORED BREATHING, A GURGLING GASP...
I CAME TO MY FEET AND LURCHED THROUGH THE DOORWAY--AND THEN FOR ONE CATACLYSMIC MOMENT I WAS ROOTED TO THE SPOT, UNABLE TO MOVE, TO CRY OUT...

A MOULDERING SKELETON SAT ASTRIDE AMOS STARK, ITS BONY ARMS BOWED ABOVE HIS THROAT, ITS FINGERS AT HIS NECK, AND IN THE BACK OF HIS SKULL WERE SHATTERED BONES, WHERE A CHARGE OF SHOT HAD GONE THROUGH. THEN, MERCIFULLY, I FAINTED.

WHEN I CAME TO MOMENTS LATER, HE LAY WHERE I HAD LAST SEEN HIM. DECENCY IMPELLED ME TO PAUSE AT AMOS STARK'S SIDE, TO SEE IF HE WAS BEYOND ALL HELP.
IT WAS THAT FATEFUL PAUSE WHICH BROUGHT THE CROWNING HORROR OF ALL, FOR AS I BENT OVER STARK, I SAW STICKING INTO THE DISCOLORED FLESH OF HIS NECK THE WHITENED FINGERBONES OF A SKELETON...

EVEN AS I LOOKED UPON THEM, THE INDIVIDUAL BONES DETACHED THEM-SELVES AND WENT BOUNDING AWAY FROM THE CORPSE, DOWN THE HALL, AND OUT INTO THE NIGHT TO REJOIN THAT GHASTLY VISITOR WHO HAD COME FROM THE GRAVE TO KEEP HIS APPOINTMENT WITH AMOS STARK!
RUSS JONES- 66
THE END

THE PAST MASTER

ROBERT BLOCH

Adapter: CRAIG TENNIS

Artist: ALDEN McWILLIAMS

ROBERT BLOCH'S

The Past Master

Luigi's

CRAIG TENNIS
A. McWILLIAMS
COLD WAR TENSIONS GET HOTTER, AND POPULAR FEAR GETS COLDER, BUT LIFE GOES ON...

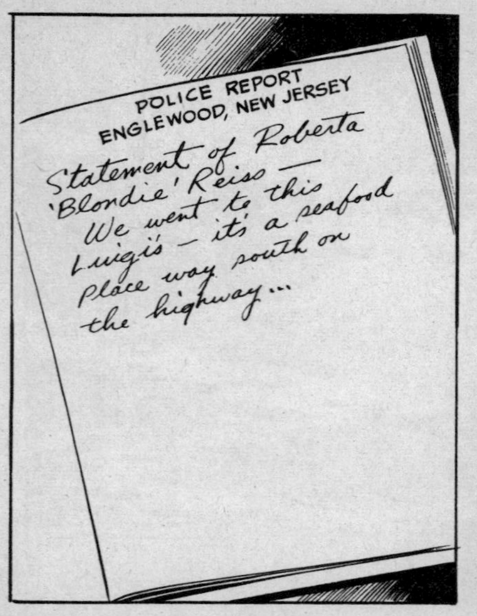

POLICE REPORT
ENGLEWOOD, NEW JERSEY

Statement of Roberta 'Blondie' Reiss — We went to this Luigi's – it's a seafood place way south on the highway...

LOOK AT THAT FULL MOON. ISN'T IT BEAUTIFUL?
LET'S GO DOWN ON THE BEACH. I KNOW A LITTLE COVE WHERE WE CAN BE ALONE.
COME ON, BABY.
NOW CUT THAT OUT! I MEAN IT--I'LL SOCK YOU ONE!
I'M SORRY, HONEY. I DON'T KNOW WHAT CAME OVER ME. I KNOW YOU'RE NOT THAT KIND OF GIRL...
YOU TORE MY BLOUSE! YOU'LL HAVE TO PAY FOR IT!

WHY DON'T I GO GET ANOTHER BOTTLE? OR LET'S BOTH GO TO A TAVERN.
I'M NOT GOING ANYWHERE LOOKING LIKE THIS! IF YOU WANT ANOTHER BOTTLE, YOU GO GET IT--AND BE BACK HERE IN FIVE MINUTES!

SOMETHING'S MOVING OUT THERE ... A LOG OR SOMETHING. NO, IT'S SOMEONE SWIMMING, REAL FAST.

I SAT ALONE ... WAITING FOR HIM TO COME OUT OF THE WATER AND GO AWAY...
...ONLY HE DIDN'T LEAVE... AND HE DIDN'T HAVE A STITCH ON!

GOOD EVENING. MIGHT I INQUIRE ABOUT MY WHEREABOUTS, MISS? AND MIGHT I TROUBLE YOU FOR THE LOAN OF THAT BLANKET?

I LOST MY SWIM SUIT IN THE BREAKERS.
WHERE DID YOU START FROM? YOU GOT A BOAT OUT THERE?
BUT BEFORE HE ANSWERED, GEORGE CAME RUNNING DOWN FROM THE BLUFF...
HEY! WHAT'S THE BIG IDEA? GIMME THAT BLANKET!
HE CAN'T! HE HASN'T ANY BATHING SUIT.
PERMIT ME TO INTRODUCE MYSELF...
I MUST ADMIT THAT GEORGE STOOD UP TO THE BIG MAN...
YOU'RE COMING WITH US THEN, FELLA. HE'S PROBABLY ONE OF THOSE RUSSIAN SPIES FROM A SUBMARINE. START TALKING, WHAT'S IN THE BAG?

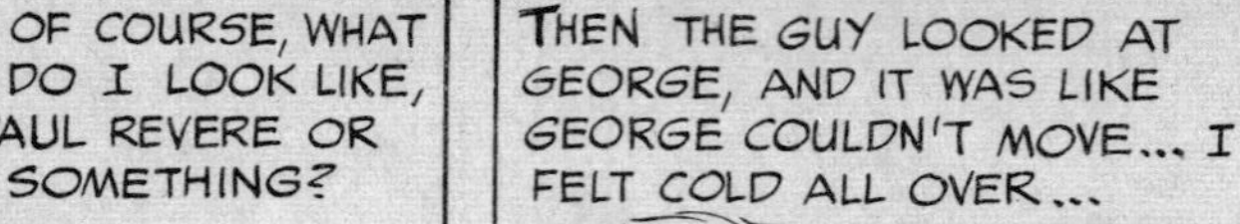
YOU HAVE AN AUTOMOBILE?
OF COURSE, WHAT DO I LOOK LIKE, PAUL REVERE OR SOMETHING?

THEN THE GUY LOOKED AT GEORGE, AND IT WAS LIKE GEORGE COULDN'T MOVE... I FELT COLD ALL OVER...

THEN THE MAN WENT OVER TO GEORGE AND TOOK ALL HIS CLOTHES AND PUT THEM ON HIMSELF!

WITHOUT A WORD, THE MAN CLIMBED INTO GEORGE'S CAR AND DROVE AWAY.

ONCE HE WAS OUT OF SIGHT I SCREAMED TILL I THOUGHT I'D HEMORRHAGE OR SOMETHING. THAT BROUGHT GEORGE OUT OF IT.

WE WALKED ALL THE WAY TO THE HIGHWAY PATROL.
YOU MAY BE RIGHT ABOUT THE COMMUNISTS...
ONLY HE HADN'T SEEN THE WAY THE MAN HAD LOOKED AT GEORGE. WHEN I THINK ABOUT IT, I COULD JUST DIE!

WESTCHESTER COUNTY
N.Y. POLICE REPORT N.Y.
Statement of Milo Fabian.
Occupation: Art Gallery Curator.
... I had just barely opened up when he walked in...
IS THIS THE WARLOCK GALLERY?
YES. MR. WARLOCK IS OUT OF TOWN. I'M MILO FABIAN. IF YOU HAVE ANYTHING TO SELL, SHOW IT TO ME. I DO ALL THE BUYING.
BUT THE MAN WANTED TO BUY!
AS YOU PROBABLY KNOW, WE SPECIALIZE IN MODERNS.
YOU DON'T HAVE THE PICTURES I WANT, I'M AFRAID.

THEN WHAT WAS IT YOU WISHED?
TWO REMBRANDTS, A RAPHAEL, A TITIAN AND SOMETHING BY VAN GOGH. ALSO A GOYA, AN EL GRECO, A GAUGUIN. I DON'T SUPPOSE THERE'S A WAY OF GETTING 'THE LAST SUPPER' OFF THE CHAPEL WALL, IS THERE?
I'M AFRAID I WAS PIQUED...
PLEASE! I'M VERY BUSY THIS MORNING. I HAVE NO TIME--
I WANT YOU TO ACT AS MY AGENT. I'VE GOT MONEY.
THE PLASTIC POUCH HE UNZIPPED WAS FULL OF FIVE AND TEN THOUSAND DOLLAR BILLS!
WELL, DO YOU THINK I HAVE ENOUGH?

I WAS FINALLY ABLE TO SPEAK...
YOU — YOU'RE REALLY SERIOUS ABOUT THIS?
I'LL WRITE DOWN THE NAMES OF WHAT I WANT YOU TO BUY FOR ME.
AND HE DID: DEGAS, UTRILLO, MONET, TOULOUSE-LAUTREC...
REALLY...YOU CAN'T EXPECT TO BUY THE "MONA LISA"-- IT'S NOT FOR SALE AT ANY PRICE.
OH- I DIDN'T KNOW.
THEN HE DROPPED A BLOCK-BUSTER...
I'VE GOT TO HAVE EVERYTHING BY SUNDAY NIGHT.
BUT THIS IS TUESDAY!

I'M BEGINNING TO UNDERSTAND ... ALL THESE THINGS ARE SCATTERED OVER THE WORLD. HOW MANY ARE HERE IN THE UNITED STATES?
WELL OVER HALF.

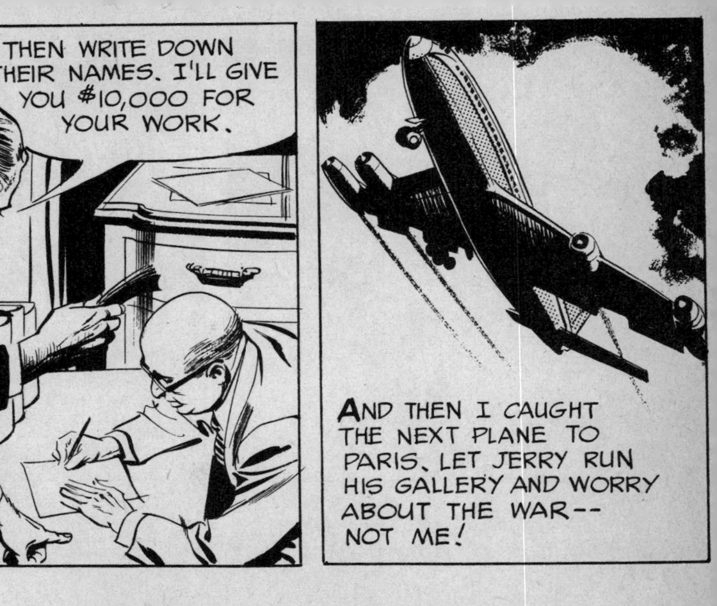
THEN WRITE DOWN THEIR NAMES. I'LL GIVE YOU $10,000 FOR YOUR WORK.
AND THEN I CAUGHT THE NEXT PLANE TO PARIS. LET JERRY RUN HIS GALLERY AND WORRY ABOUT THE WAR-- NOT ME!

POLICE REPORT
U.S. Coast Guard Shore Patrol Report, Statement of Nick Krauss, alias Herman Krueger, alias...
... I started on the caper Tuesday nite... It was the biggest payoff ever rigged, I got six million bucks in four days, and brother, I earned every cent of it!...
HE CAME INTO MY OFFICE -- I DON'T KNOW HOW HE GOT PAST MY MEN... WE MADE A DEAL...
I'VE GOT A JOB FOR YOU. HERE'S 2 MILLION FOR EXPENSES. THERE'S 4 MILLION MORE IF YOU COÖPERATE.
I HAD GUYS WITH CASH FLYING TO DETROIT, CHICAGO, PHILADELPHIA AND BOSTON...

THE METROPOLITAN MUSEUM FIRST ACQUIRED THIS PICASSO...
PAY OFF THE GUARDS, THE COPPERS AND THE GUYS WHO RUN THE MUSEUMS, TOO. GIVE THEM A LOT. THEY'LL RAT ON YOU FOR 2 OR 3 G'S, BUT THEY'RE YOURS FOR 20 OR 30 GRAND...

OF COURSE WE RAN INTO SOME TROUBLE. WE NEVER DID GET THE HAUL OUT OF L.A. BUT LUCKILY THE COPS SHOT UP THE GUYS SO THEY COULDN'T TRACE ANYTHING... OTHER PLACES WE GOT AWAY CLEAN...

ALL THE STUFF CAME INTO NEW JERSEY BY PRIVATE PLANE...
GET THAT JUNK INTO THE WARE-HOUSE!

IT TOOK ME THREE HOURS TO GET IT ALL TO SMITH'S BOAT...
THAT'S THE WORKS, SMITH. YOU SATISFIED OR YOU WANT A RECEIPT?
YOU'LL HAVE TO OPEN THEM UP.

MISTER, THAT STUFF'S HOT AND I'M HOTTER. THERE'S MAYBE 10,000 JOHNS LOOKING FOR THIS LOOT... AIN'T YOU READ THE PAPERS! IT'S BIGGER THAN THE WAR CRISIS. NOW I WANT OUT OF HERE--FAST.

BUT HE WANTED THEM CRATES AND BOXES OPEN...
I GUESS FOR 4 MILLION BUCKS, A LITTLE FLUNKY WORK WON'T HURT...
NONE SEEMS TO BE DAMAGED-- YOU DID A GOOD JOB.
IT TOOK THREE MORE HOURS, BUT I FINISHED...
WHAT'S THE PITCH? WHERE ARE YOU GOING?
TO TRANSFER THEM TO MY SHIP. I'LL NEED YOUR ASSISTANCE.
HE STARTED THE ENGINES AND I STUCK MY SPECIAL IN HIS RIBS.
WHERE'S THE BUNDLE?
IN THE CABIN. ...SEE FOR YOURSELF.

FOUR MILLION BUCKS ON THE BUNK IN 5 AND 10 THOUSAND DOLLAR BILLS, AND NO PHONY GEETUS EITHER...
I RETURNED TO HIM, MY SUSPICIONS GONE...
I'LL HELP YOU, BUT THE FIRST TIME YOU GET CUTE I'LL TAKE OUT YOUR APPENDIX WITH A SLUG.
WE HAVE TO GO ABOUT 5 MILES.
SMITH CUT THE ENGINES AND DROPPED ANCHOR...
WHERE'S YOUR BOAT?.. I DON'T SEE NOTHING...

IT'S DOWN THERE.
YOU GOT A SUBMARINE OR SOMETHING?

THEN HE RAISED HIS HAND AND THIS BIG ROUND SILVER BALL, POPS UP!!

THEN A DOOR SLIDES OPEN AND SMITH LAYS A PLANK ACROSS TO THE OPENING.
YOU THINK I'M CRAZY ENOUGH TO WALK ON THAT? IN THE DARK.
YOU CAN'T FALL-- IT'S MAGNO-MESHED.
WHATEVER THAT MEANT...
IF HE WAS A COMMUNIST, I THOUGHT I'D BETTER HAVE A LOOK AT HIS SUB!
WHERE'S THE ENGINE?
WE'RE NOT FINISHED LOADING YET.
AS I KEPT LOADING, I GOT MORE SCARED...
HE'S NO RUSSIAN, AND THERE AIN'T NO BALLS THAT FLOAT UP OUT OF THE WATER WHEN YOU JUST WAVE YOUR HAND.

YOU CAN LEAVE WHENEVER YOU LIKE... TAKE THE BOAT.
LEAVE? I CAN'T RUN THIS YACHT!

IT'S EASY, I'LL SHOW YOU HOW.
NO YOU DON'T... TAKE ME BACK. THEN GO OFF TO MARS, OR WHEREVER IT IS...

MARS? WHO SAID ANY-THING ABOUT...
THE LAST THING I REMEMBER WAS PULLING THE TRIGGER.

LONG ISLAND POLICE REPORT

Following statement of
Elizabeth Rafferty, M.D.

I guess in this world of
continuous crises we become
immune to war scares, for
on this night the radio
commentators were more
concerned with the pilfered
art Treasures. Nearly
every valuable piece of
art work was missing,
and the police were
watching in particular
the coast where I
lived. Naturally I
was suspicious....

YOUR ARM WILL BE STIFF FOR SEVERAL DAYS... HOW DID IT HAPPEN?
A HUNTING ACCIDENT.

YOU KNOW I HAVE TO MAKE OUT A REPORT ON ANY GUNSHOT WOUNDS.

I'M LEAVING NOW. PERHAPS THIS FEE WILL PERSUADE YOU THAT I'VE NEVER BEEN HERE.
FIFTEEN THOUSAND DOLLARS?

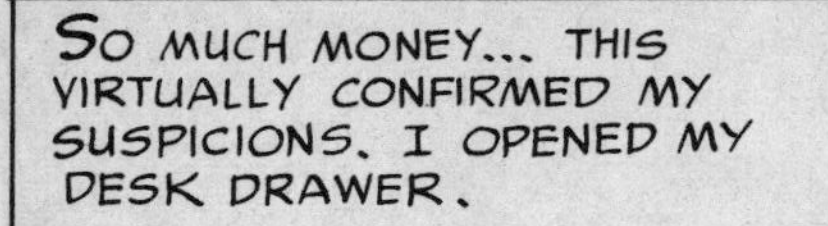

SO MUCH MONEY... THIS VIRTUALLY CONFIRMED MY SUSPICIONS. I OPENED MY DESK DRAWER.
THIS IS ONLY A LADY'S GUN, MR. SMITH, BUT I'M AN EXPERT WITH IT. HANDS UP WHILE I PHONE THE POLICE.
I HAVE NO WEAPON, DOCTOR...

TAKE THE MONEY AND FORGET THE REPORT...
IT'S TEMPTING, BUT NO SALE... WHERE ARE THE PAINTINGS, MR. SMITH?

YOU'RE BEING FOOLISH TO DELAY, BELIEVE ME.
BELIEVE YOU, WITH THE ENTIRE COUNTRY IN AN UPROAR OVER COMMUNISTS AND STOLEN MASTERPIECES?

I COULD SHOW YOU THE PAINTINGS, BUT WITHIN 24 HOURS THEY'LL BE AS USELESS AS YOUR REPORT.
THE WAY YOU TALK, YOU'D THINK THE BOMBS WERE GOING TO DROP TOMORROW.
THEY WILL, HERE AND EVERYWHERE ELSE.
I IGNORED HIM... I'D SEEN NAPOLEONIC COMPLEXES BEFORE.
WHAT IS YOUR REAL NAME AND DATE OF BIRTH...
KIM RA... NOV. 25, 2903

STOP BEING RIDICULOUS... WHY DID YOU STEAL THE PAINTINGS?
THE WAR IS COMING TOMORROW, BUT I WILL HAVE SAVED THE MASTERPIECES... YOU MUST UNDER-STAND, I KNOW BECAUSE I'M NOT OF YOUR TIME OR PLANET.
SUPPOSE I GO ALONG WITH YOUR CLAIM... HOW CAN THE PAINTINGS BE WITH YOU WHEN YOU RETURN TO YOUR TIME PERIOD?
SURELY THEY CAN'T PHYSICALLY EXIST IN TWO PERIODS AT THE SAME TIME.
WHY NOT...I WAS WOUNDED IN THIS TIME PERIOD, YET I DON'T BELONG HERE.

EVEN IF YOU'RE TELLING THE TRUTH, I CAN'T ADMIRE YOUR MOTIVES.
WHY? ISN'T IT WORTHWHILE TO SAVE PRICELESS TREASURES FROM A SENSELESS TRIBAL WAR?
BECAUSE, IF YOU KNOW SO MUCH, YOU SHOULD SAVE THE WORLD INSTEAD!
I CAN'T PREVENT ITS DESTRUCTION... NONE OF OUR RECORDS TELL HOW THE WAR WILL START... SOME TRIVIAL INCIDENT PROBABLY AND I CAN'T CHANGE HISTORY.
AREN'T YOU CHANGING IT BY TAKING THE PICTURES?

THE TIME... I MUST GET GOING...
YOU'RE RIGHT, TIME'S UP... NOW I'M GOING TO CALL THE POLICE...

WAIT! I'LL EVEN TAKE YOU WITH ME... YOU'LL ESCAPE!
ME? INTO ANOTHER TIME ZONE? THE JOKE'S OVER...

THEN HE SMILED AT ME. I THOUGHT I WAS ENTIRELY IMMUNE TO HYPNOTISM, BUT I WAS WRONG.

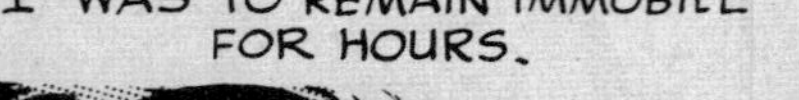

I KNEW NOW SMITH HAD BEEN TELLING THE TRUTH, BUT WHERE HAD HE GONE? WHO WOULD BELIEVE MY WILD EXPERIENCE.

SUDDENLY, A ROUND BALL ROSE OUT OF THE OCEAN... JUST OFF THE BOW OF A COAST GUARD CUTTER...

THE CUTTER BLASTED THE SILVER BALL INTO DUST... AND THE SHIP'S CAPTAIN REPORTED TO HIS SUPERIOR IMMEDIATELY.
WE JUST DESTROYED SOME NEW TYPE OF SOVIET WEAPON!
THEN I'M CALLING FOR AN ALL-OUT RETALIATION!
WHAT HAD SMITH SAID? SOME TRIVIAL INCIDENT? WELL, THIS WAS THE TRIVIAL INCIDENT THAT STARTED THE WAR
The End

THE DEATH OF HALPIN FRAYSER

AMBROSE BIERCE

Adapter: CRAIG TENNIS

Artist: FRANK BOLLE

I
"...IT IS KNOWN THAT SOME SPIRITS
WHICH IN LIFE WERE BENIGN BECOME
BY DEATH EVIL ALTOGETHER."
—HALI
THE DEATH of HALPIN FRAYSER
by AMBROSE BIERCE

ONE DARK MIDSUMMER NIGHT, HALPIN, WAKING FROM A DREAMLESS SLEEP, SPOKE A NAME AND NOTHING MORE ...
... CATHERINE LARUE.
FRANK BOLLE

HALPIN FRAYSER LIVED IN ST. HELENA, CALIFORNIA. BUT WHERE HE LIVES NOW IS UNCERTAIN, FOR HE IS LONG DEAD.
I WON'T LIVE LONG IF I KEEP THIS UP!
HE HAD LOST HIS WAY WHILE HUNTING WHEN THE AFTER-NOON HAD BECOME CLOUDY...
HOW ODD, TO SPEAK A NAME I KNOW NOT...
HE WENT BACK TO SLEEP, BUT IT WAS NO LONGER DREAMLESS.

IN HIS DREAM HE CAME TO A PARTING OF THE WAYS...
...WITHOUT HESITATION HE TURNED INTO THE EVIL ROAD.
FROM AMONG THE TREES ON EITHER SIDE HE CAUGHT BROKEN AND INCOHERENT WHISPERS. THEY SEEMED FRAGMENTARY UTTERANCES OF A MONSTROUS CONSPIRACY AGAINST HIS BODY AND SOUL.

LONG AFTER NIGHTFALL THE INTERMINABLE FOREST WAS LIT WITH A WAN GLIMMER.
BLOOD! IT'S BLOOD EVERYWHERE!
THE WEEDS GROWING RANKLY SHOWED IT IN BLOTS AND SPLASHES ON THEIR LEAVES. PATCHES OF DRY DUST WERE PITTED AS WITH A RED RAIN. THE TREES WERE MACULATIONS OF CRIMSON, AND BLOOD DRIPPED LIKE DEW...

I WILL NOT SUBMIT! I SHALL LEAVE A RECORD AND AN APPEAL. I SHALL RELATE MY WRONGS, THE PERSECUTIONS THAT I ENDURE -- I, A HELPLESS MORTAL, A PENTINENT, AN UNOFFENDING POET!

HALPIN WAS A POET ONLY AS HE WAS A PENTINENT, IN HIS DREAM.

HALPIN BROKE A TWIG AND WROTE RAPIDLY WITH BLOODY INK.

HE-HE-HO-HO

HAW-HAW-AHH!

IN THE MIDDLE OF A SENTENCE HIS HANDS DENIED THEIR SERVICE TO HIS WILL...
I MUST COMPLETE MY APPEAL SHOULD THIS TORTURE CONTINUE, AND I BE DENIED THE BLESSING OF ANNIHILATION!
HE FOUND HIMSELF STARING INTO THE EYES OF HIS OWN--
MOTHER!

II
IN HIS YOUTH, HALPIN FRAYSER HAD LIVED WITH HIS PARENTS IN NASHVILLE, TENNESSEE.
YOUR MATERNAL GREAT-GRANDFATHER WROTE THESE. HE WAS A POET OF NO SMALL COLONIAL DISTINCTION. BE PROUD OF HIM AND YOUR HERITAGE.
POEMS MYRON BAYNE
I AM, FOR I KNOW THAT ONLY YOU AND I APPRECIATE HIM.
BUT HALPIN, HIMSELF, COULD NOT HAVE WRITTEN A LINE OF VERSE TO SAVE HIMSELF...

THE ATTACHMENT BETWEEN THE TWO BECAME YEARLY STRONGER AND MORE TENDER.
...ATTRACTIVE LOVERS...
WOULD YOU MIND GREATLY, KATY, IF I WERE CALLED AWAY TO CALIFORNIA FOR A FEW WEEKS?
I SHOULD HAVE KNOWN THIS WAS COMING...

I DREAMED GRANDFATHER BAYNE HAD COME TO ME, AND STANDING BY HIS PORTRAIT, POINTED TO YOURS AND WHEN I LOOKED YOUR FACE WAS COVERED BY A DEATH CLOTH.
YOUR FATHER LAUGHED AT ME, BUT YOU AND I KNOW SUCH THINGS ARE NOT FOR NOTHING... BELOW THE CLOTH I SAW THE MARKS OF HANDS ON YOUR THROAT.

ARE THERE MEDICINAL SPRINGS IN CALIFORNIA? MY FINGERS FEEL SO STIFF...

THESE TWO ODD PEOPLE, HAVING EQUALLY ODD NOTIONS OF DUTY, PARTED. ONE WENT TO CALIFORNIA FOR A CLIENT, THE OTHER STAYED HOME WITH HER HUSBAND.

IN SAN FRANCISCO, HALPIN WAS "SHANGHAIED" AND BECAME A SAILOR. MISFORTUNE GREW AND HE WAS SHIPWRECKED FOR SIX YEARS BEFORE BEING RESCUED...
THOUGH POOR IN PURSE, HE WAS PROUD IN SPIRIT AND WOULD ACCEPT NO HELP. WITH A FELLOW SURVIVOR HE WENT TO ST. HELENA TO HUNT AND DREAM... AND AWAIT NEWS FROM HOME.

III
THE APPARITION CONFRONTING THE DREAMER STIRRED NO LOVE OR LONGING IN HIS HEART. HE TRIED TO TURN AND RUN FROM BEFORE IT, BUT COULD NOT.
A BODY WITHOUT A SOUL!
WHAT MORTAL CAN COPE WITH A CREATURE OF HIS DREAMS?
THEN ALL WAS BLACK. A SOUND OF THE BEATING OF DISTANT DRUMS--A MURMUR OF SWARMING VOICES, AND HALPIN FRAYSER DREAMED THAT HE WAS DEAD.

IV
AT ABOUT TWO O'CLOCK ON THE PRECEDING DAY, THE GHOST OF A CLOUD HAD BEEN OBSERVED ON MOUNT ST. HELENA.
LOOK AT THE CLOUD BEING BORN, QUICKLY, BEFORE IT GOES AWAY!
BUT IN A MOMENT IT WAS VISIBLY LARGER AND DENSER...
HOW FAR IS IT, JARALSON?
THE WHITE CHURCH? A HALF MILE FARTHER.

BY THE WAY, HOLKER, IT'S NOT A CHURCH, BUT AN ABANDONED SCHOOL-HOUSE, AND NEARBY IS A GRAVEYARD THAT WOULD DELIGHT A POET... DO YOU KNOW WHY I SENT FOR YOU?
YOU WANT ME TO HELP YOU ARREST A CORPSE?
DO YOU REMEMBER 'BRANSCOM,' DETECTIVE?
THE CHAP WHO CUT HIS WIFE'S THROAT, OF COURSE. $500 REWARD ON HIM. YOU DON'T MEAN TO SAY–
HE'S BEEN UNDER YOUR NOSE ALL THE TIME. BY NIGHT HE COMES TO THE OLD GRAVEYARD.

THE DEVIL! THAT'S WHERE THEY BURIED HIS WIFE! YOU FOUND HIM?
HE FOUND ME! THE RASCAL GOT THE DROP, HELD ME UP AND MADE ME TRAVEL.
THERE'S GLORY IN IT FOR US. NOT ANOTHER SOUL KNOWS HE'S HERE.
BY THE WAY, I HEARD 'BRANSCOM' ISN'T HIS REAL NAME. IT'S 'PARDEE OR SOMETHING. THE WOMAN WAS WIDOWED AND HAD COME TO CALIFORNIA TO LOOK UP A RELATIVE.

HOW DID YOU FIND THE GRAVE?
I DIDN'T. I HAD BEEN WATCHING THE PLACE GENERALLY.

I WILL SHOW YOU WHERE HE HELD ME UP.

THE PATHS, IF ANY PATHS HAD BEEN WERE LONG OBLITERATED.
IT WAS RIGHT OVER HERE...

NOT A NICE PLACE TO SPEND AN EVENING...
HUH?

POOR DEVIL!
THE WORK OF A MANIAC. IT WAS DONE BY 'BRANSCOM' OR 'PARDEE,' OR WHOEVER HE IS.
LISTEN TO THIS:
"ENTHRALLED BY SOME MYSTERIOUS SPELL, I STOOD IN THE LIT GLOOM OF ENCHANTED WOOD, THE CYPRESS THERE AND MYRTLE TWINED THEIR BOUGHS, SIGNIFICANT, IN BALEFUL BROTHERHOOD."

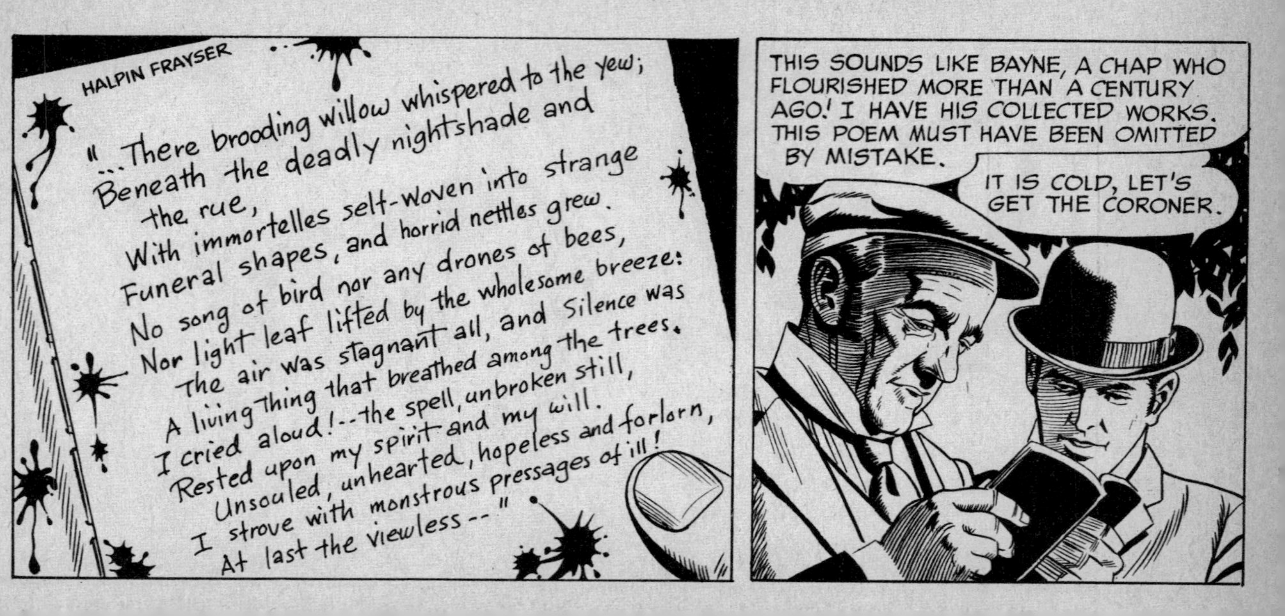
HALPIN FRAYSER
"...There brooding willow whispered to the yew;
Beneath the deadly nightshade and
the rue,
With immortelles self-woven into strange
Funeral shapes, and horrid nettles grew.
No song of bird nor any drones of bees,
Nor light leaf lifted by the wholesome breeze:
The air was stagnant all, and Silence was
A living thing that breathed among the trees.
I cried aloud!--the spell, unbroken still,
Rested upon my spirit and my will.
Unsouled, unhearted, hopeless and forlorn,
I strove with monstrous pressages of ill!
At last the viewless--"
THIS SOUNDS LIKE BAYNE, A CHAP WHO FLOURISHED MORE THAN A CENTURY AGO! I HAVE HIS COLLECTED WORKS. THIS POEM MUST HAVE BEEN OMITTED BY MISTAKE.
IT IS COLD, LET'S GET THE CORONER.

OUCH!
WHAT'S THAT?
'LARUE'--THAT'S THE REAL NAME OF 'BRANSCOM', AND NOW IT COMES BACK, THE WOMAN'S NAME WAS 'FRAYSER' BEFORE--THE SAME NAME AS IN THE NOTEBOOK!.
CATHERINE LARUE

THERE IS SOME RASCALLY MYSTERY HERE... I HATE ANYTHING OF THAT KIND.
THERE CAME TO THEM OUT OF THE FOG THE SOUND OF A LAUGH, A LAUGH THAT ROSE BY GRADUAL DEGREES...
HE-HE-HO-HO-HA-HA-HAW-HAW-WHU-HU
THEN IT DIED AWAY, JOYLESS AND MECHANICAL TO THE LAST, SINKING TO SILENCE AT A MEASURELESS REMOVE.

THE END

DRACULA'S GUEST

BRAM STOKER

Adapter: E. NELSON BRIDWELL

Artist: FRANK BOLLE

DRACULA'S GUEST
BY BRAM STOKER
THIS STORY WAS INTENDED AS THE OPENING EPISODE IN BRAM STOKER'S NOVEL, **DRACULA**, BUT WAS EXCISED BECAUSE OF THE LENGTH OF THE BOOK. AS READERS OF **DRACULA** WILL RECALL, IT OPENS WITH THE ENTRY FOR MAY 3 IN THE JOURNAL OF JONATHAN HARKER, A YOUNG ENGLISH SOLICITOR, ON HIS WAY TO TRANSACT BUSINESS WITH A CLIENT IN TRANSYLVANIA -- COUNT DRACULA. BUT LET US GO BACK AND READ THE ENTRY FOR MAY 1 ...

FRANK BOLLE

WHEN WE STARTED FOR OUR DRIVE THE SUN WAS SHINING BRIGHTLY IN MUNICH. HERR DELBRÜCK (THE MAÎTRE D'HOTEL OF THE QUATRE SAISONS, WHERE I WAS STAYING) CAME DOWN AND, AFTER WISHING ME A PLEASANT DRIVE...
JA, MEIN HERR.
REMEMBER YOU ARE BACK BY NIGHTFALL. THIS IS A SHIVER IN THE WIND THAT SAYS THERE MAY BE A SUDDEN STORM. BUT YOU WILL NOT BE LATE, FOR YOU KNOW WHAT NIGHT IT IS.
JOHANN DROVE OFF QUICKLY. WHEN WE HAD CLEARED THE TOWN, I SIGNALED HIM TO STOP.
TELL ME, JOHANN, WHAT IS TONIGHT?
WALPURGIS NACHT.

CROSSING HIMSELF, HE STARTED OFF RAPIDLY, AS IF TO MAKE UP FOR LOST TIME. EVERY NOW AND THEN THE HORSES SEEMED TO THROW UP THEIR HEADS AND SNIFFED THE AIR SUSPICIOUSLY.
ON SUCH OCCASIONS I OFTEN LOOKED AROUND IN ALARM. WE WERE TRAVERSING A HIGH, WIND-SWEPT PLATEAU. THEN I SAW A ROAD WHICH SEEMED TO DIP THROUGH A LITTLE, WINDING VALLEY.

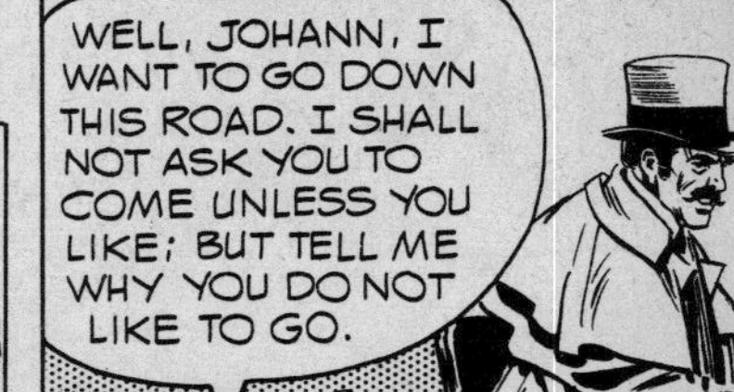
I CALLED JOHANN TO STOP--AND TOLD HIM I WOULD LIKE TO DRIVE DOWN THAT ROAD. HE MADE ALL SORTS OF EXCUSES AND FRE-QUENTLY CROSSED HIMSELF. FINALLY...
WELL, JOHANN, I WANT TO GO DOWN THIS ROAD. I SHALL NOT ASK YOU TO COME UNLESS YOU LIKE; BUT TELL ME WHY YOU DO NOT LIKE TO GO.

HE THREW HIMSELF OFF THE BOX AND IMPLORED ME NOT TO GO. HE SEEMED ALWAYS JUST ABOUT TO TELL ME SOMETHING WHICH FRIGHTENED HIM; BUT EACH TIME HE PULLED HIMSELF UP, SAYING, AS HE CROSSED HIMSELF:

THEN THE HORSES BECAME RESTLESS AND SNIFFED THE AIR. AT THIS HE SUDDENLY JUMPED FORWARD, TOOK THEM BY THE BRIDLES AND LED THEM ON SOME TWENTY FEET.

I FOLLOWED, AND ASKED WHY HE HAD DONE THIS. HE POINTED TO THE SPOT WE HAD LEFT AND DREW HIS CARRIAGE IN THE DIRECTION OF THE OTHER ROAD, INDICATING A CROSS.

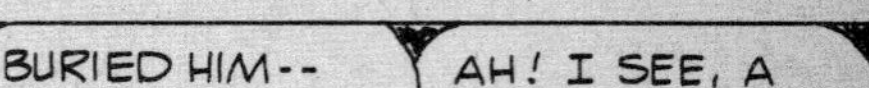

WHILST WE WERE TALKING, WE HEARD A SORT OF SOUND BETWEEN A YELP AND A BARK. IT WAS FAR AWAY; BUT THE HORSES GOT VERY RESTLESS, AND IT TOOK JOHANN ALL HIS TIME TO QUIET THEM.
IT SOUNDS LIKE A WOLF-- BUT YET THERE ARE NO WOLVES HERE NOW.
REMARKING THAT THE SNOW STORM WOULD SOON COME, JOHANN CLIMBED TO HIS BOX AS THOUGH THE TIME HAD COME FOR PROCEEDING ON OUR JOURNEY. I DID NOT AT ONCE GET INTO THE CARRIAGE.
TELL ME ABOUT THIS PLACE WHERE THE ROAD LEADS.
IT IS UNHOLY. THE VILLAGE. NO ONE LIVES THERE HUNDREDS OF YEARS.

"MEN DIED THERE AND WERE BURIED: AND SOUNDS WERE HEARD UNDER THE CLAY, AND WHEN THE GRAVES WERE OPENED, MEN AND WOMEN WERE FOUND ROSY WITH LIFE, AND THEIR MOUTHS RED WITH BLOOD."
AND SO, IN HASTE TO SAVE THEIR LIVES (AYE, AND THEIR SOULS!) THOSE WHO WERE LEFT FLED AWAY TO OTHER PLACES, WHERE THE LIVING LIVED, AND THE DEAD WERE DEAD AND NOT--NOT SOMETHING ELSE. GET IN! WALPURGIS NACHT!

ALL MY ENGLISH BLOOD ROSE AT THIS. I TOOK FROM THE SEAT MY OAK WALKING STICK AND CLOSED THE DOOR, POINTING BACK TO MUNICH.
YOU ARE AFRAID, JOHANN. GO HOME; I SHALL RETURN ALONE; THE WALK WILL DO ME GOOD. WALPURGIS NACHT DOES NOT CONCERN ENGLISHMEN.
WITH A DESPAIRING GESTURE JOHANN TURNED HIS HORSES TOWARD MUNICH. HE WENT SLOWLY ALONG THE ROAD FOR A WHILE; THEN THERE CAME OVER THE CREST OF THE HILL A MAN TALL AND THIN.

WHEN HE DREW NEAR THE HORSES, THEY BEGAN TO JUMP AND KICK ABOUT, THEN TO SCREAM WITH TERROR. JOHANN COULD NOT HOLD THEM; THEY BOLTED DOWN THE ROAD, RUNNING AWAY MADLY.
I WATCHED THEM OUT OF SIGHT, THEN LOOKED FOR THE STRANGER, BUT FOUND THAT HE, TOO, WAS GONE.

I TURNED DOWN THE SIDE ROAD THROUGH THE DEEPENING VALLEY. I TRAMPED FOR A COUPLE OF HOURS WITHOUT SEEING A PERSON OR A HOUSE. ON TURNING A BEND IN THE ROAD, I CAME UPON A SCATTERED FRINGE OF WOOD; THEN I RECOGNIZED THAT I HAD BEEN SUBCONSCIOUSLY IMPRESSED BY THE DESOLATION OF THE REGION THROUGH WHICH I HAD PASSED.

I SAT DOWN TO REST MYSELF AND BEGAN TO LOOK AROUND. GREAT THICK CLOUDS WERE DRIFTING RAPIDLY ACROSS THE SKY. THERE WERE SIGNS OF COMING STORM IN THE AIR. I WAS A LITTLE CHILLY, AND, THINKING IT WAS THE SITTING STILL, I RESUMED MY JOURNEY.

THE GROUND I PASSED OVER WAS NOW MUCH MORE PICTURESQUE. IT WAS ONLY WHEN THE DEEPENING TWILIGHT FORCED ITSELF UPON ME THAT I BEGAN TO THINK OF HOW I SHOULD FIND MY WAY HOME. THE DRIFTING OF CLOUDS WAS ACCOMPANIED BY A FAR-AWAY RUSHING SOUND, THROUGH WHICH SEEMED TO COME THE CRY OF A WOLF.
I PRESENTLY CAME ON A WIDE STRETCH OF OPEN COUNTRY, SHUT IN BY HILLS ALL AROUND. AS I LOOKED THE SNOW BEGAN TO FALL. SOON THE EARTH AROUND ME WAS A GLISTENING WHITE CARPET. IN FLASHES OF VIVID LIGHTNING I COULD SEE AHEAD OF ME A GREAT MASS OF TREES.

I WAS SOON IN THE SHELTER OF THE TREES. BY AND BY THE STORM SEEMED TO BE PASSING AWAY. WHEN THE SNOW HAD CEASED TO FALL, I FOUND A LOW WALL ENCIRCLING THE COPSE, AND FOLLOWING THIS I FOUND AN OPENING. HERE THE CYPRESSES FORMED AN ALLEY LEADING UP TO A BUILDING OF SOME KIND.

I GROPED MY WAY BLINDLY ON, THEN STOPPED, FOR THERE WAS A SUDDEN STILL-NESS. THE MOONLIGHT BROKE THROUGH THE CLOUDS, SHOW-ING ME THAT I WAS IN A GRAVEYARD, AND THAT THE OBJECT BEFORE ME WAS A GREAT MARBLE TOMB OF WHITE MARBLE.

WITH THE MOONLIGHT THE STORM APPEARED TO RESUME WITH A LONG, LOW HOWL, AS OF MANY WOLVES. I WALKED AROUND THE SEPULCHER. ON THE TOP OF THE TOMB, DRIVEN THROUGH THE SOLID MARBLE, WAS A GREAT IRON STAKE OR SPIKE.
COUNTESS DOLINGEN OF GRATZ
IN STYRIA
SOUGHT AND FOUND DEAD
1801

AND NOW A PERFECT TORNADO BURST UPON ME. AND THIS TIME THE STORM BORE ON ITS ICY WINGS, NOT SNOW, BUT GREAT HAILSTONES. THE ONLY SPOT THAT SEEMED TO AFFORD REFUGE WAS THE DOORWAY OF THE MARBLE TOMB.

THERE, CROUCHING AGAINST THE MASSIVE BRONZE DOOR, I GAINED A CERTAIN AMOUNT OF PROTECTION FROM THE HAILSTONES. AS I LEANED AGAINST THE DOOR, IT MOVED SLIGHTLY AND OPENED INWARD.

THE SHELTER OF EVEN A TOMB WAS WELCOME, AND I WAS ABOUT TO ENTER IT WHEN THERE CAME A FLASH OF FORKED LIGHTNING. IN THE INSTANT, I SAW A BEAUTIFUL WOMAN SEEMINGLY SLEEPING ON A BIER.

AS THE THUNDER BROKE OVERHEAD, I WAS GRASPED AS BY THE HAND OF A GIANT AND HURLED OUT INTO THE STORM.

I WAS SEIZED AGAIN IN THE GIANT-GRASP AND DRAGGED AWAY. THE LAST SIGHT THAT I REMEMBER WAS A VAGUE, WHITE, MOVING MASS, AS IF ALL THE GRAVES HAD SENT OUT THEIR SHEETED DEAD, AND THEY WERE CLOSING IN ON ME.

GRADUALLY THERE CAME A VAGUE BEGINNING OF CONSCIOUSNESS. I FELT A WARM RASPING AT MY THROAT. SOME GREAT ANIMAL WAS LYING ON ME AND NOW LICKING MY THROAT.

THROUGH MY EYELASHES I SAW ABOVE ME THE TWO GREAT FLAMING EYES OF A GIGANTIC WOLF. ITS SHARP WHITE TEETH GLEAMED IN THE GAPING RED MOUTH, AND I COULD FEEL ITS HOT BREATH FIERCE AND ACRID UPON ME.

I HEARD A LOW GROWL, FOLLOWED BY A YELP, RENEWED AGAIN AND AGAIN. THEN, FAR AWAY, I HEARD MANY VOICES CALLING IN UNISON. FROM BEYOND THE TREES CAME A TROOP OF HORSEMEN BEARING TORCHES.

THE WOLF ROSE AND MADE FOR THE CEMETARY. ONE OF THE SOLDIERS RAISED HIS CARBINE. A COMPANION KNOCKED UP HIS ARM. AND A BALL WHIZZED OVER MY HEAD. HE HAD TAKEN MY BODY FOR THAT OF THE WOLF.

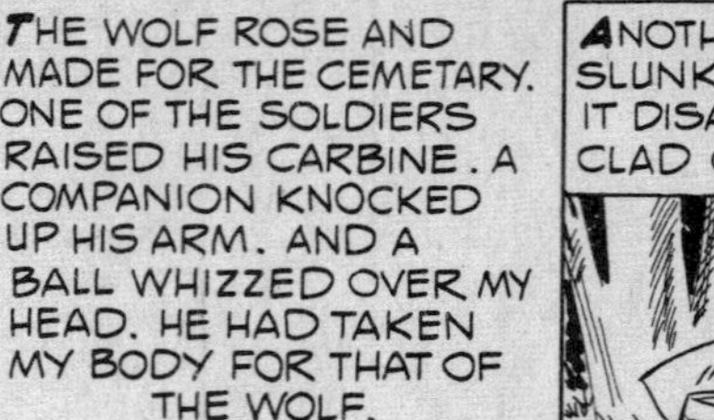
ANOTHER SIGHTED THE ANIMAL AS IT SLUNK AWAY, AND A SHOT FOLLOWED. IT DISAPPEARED AMONGST THE SNOW-CLAD CYPRESSES.

SOME OF THE SOLDIERS KNELT BESIDE ME AND POURED BRANDY DOWN MY THROAT. WHEN THE OTHERS CAME, SAYING THEY HAD NOT FOUND THE WOLF...
A WOLF -- AND YET NOT A WOLF!
NO USE TRYING FOR HIM WITHOUT THE SACRED BULLET.
THERE WAS BLOOD ON THE BROKEN MARBLE. IS HE SAFE? LOOK AT HIS THROAT! THE WOLF HAS BEEN KEEPING HIS BLOOD WARM.
THE OFFICER LOOKED AT MY THROAT.
THE SKIN IS NOT PIERCED. WHAT DOES IT ALL MEAN? WE SHOULD NEVER HAVE FOUND HIM BUT FOR THE YELPING OF THE WOLF.
LET US LEAVE THIS CURSED SPOT.

SEVERAL MEN PLACED ME UPON A HORSE. THE OFFICER SPRANG TO THE SADDLE BEHIND ME. I FELL ASLEEP; THE NEXT THING I REMEMBERED WAS FINDING MYSELF STANDING UP, SUPPORTED BY TWO SOLDIERS. IT WAS DAYLIGHT.
SAY NOTHING EXCEPT THAT WE FOUND AN ENGLISH STRANGER, GUARDED BY A LARGE DOG.
I THINK I KNOW A WOLF WHEN I SEE ONE. LOOK AT HIS THROAT. IS THAT THE WORK OF A DOG?
I RAISED MY HAND TO MY THROAT, AND AS I TOUCHED IT I CRIED OUT IN PAIN. THE MEN CROWDED ROUND TO LOOK.
OHH!
A DOG, AS I SAID. IF AUGHT ELSE WERE SAID WE SHOULD ONLY BE LAUGHED AT!

I WAS THEN MOUNTED BEHIND A TROOPER, AND WE RODE ON TO THE SUBURBS OF MUNICH. HERE WE CAME ACROSS A CARRIAGE, WHICH TOOK ME TO THE QUATRE SAISONS -- THE YOUNG OFFICER ACCOMPANYING ME.

WHEN WE ARRIVED, HERR DELBRÜCK RUSHED SO QUICKLY TO MEET ME THAT IT WAS APPARENT HE HAD BEEN WAITING. THE OFFICER SALUTED ME AND WAS TURNING TO WITHDRAW, WHEN ...
NO, NO, MY FRIEND! COME TO MY ROOMS!

OVER A GLASS OF WINE I WARMLY THANKED HIM AND HIS BRAVE COMRADES FOR SAVING ME.
I AM MORE THAN GLAD, BUT IT WAS HERR DELBRÜCK WHO TOOK THE FIRST STEPS TO MAKE ALL THE SEARCHING PARTY PLEASED.
AT THIS THE MAÎTRE D'HOTEL SMILED, WHILE THE OFFICER PLEADED DUTY AND WITHDREW.
BUT HERR DELBRÜCK, HOW AND WHY WAS IT THAT THE SOLDIERS SEARCHED FOR ME?
I OBTAINED LEAVE FROM THE COMMANDER OF THE REGIMENT IN WHICH I SERVED TO ASK FOR VOLUNTEER. THE DRIVER CAME HITHER WITH THE REMAINS OF HIS CARRIAGE, WHICH WAS UPSET WHEN THE HORSES RAN AWAY.

BUT SURELY YOU WOULD NOT SEND A SEARCH-PARTY OF SOLDIERS MERELY ON THIS ACCOUNT?
OH, NO! I HAD THIS TELEGRAM FROM THE BOYAR WHOSE GUEST YOU ARE.
TELEGRAM
BISTRITZ
BE CAREFUL OF MY GUEST. SHOULD HE BE MISSED, SPARE NOTHING TO FIND HIM AND INSURE HIS SAFETY. HE IS ENGLISH AND THEREFORE ADVENTUROUS. THERE ARE OFTEN DANGERS FROM SNOWS AND WOLVES AT NIGHT. I ANSWER YOUR ZEAL WITH MY FORTUNE.
DRACULA
THE ROOM SEEMED TO WHIRL AROUND ME. FROM A DISTANT COUNTRY HAD COME, IN THE VERY NICK OF TIME, A MESSAGE THAT TOOK ME OUT OF THE JAWS OF THE WOLF.
THUS BEGAN THE WORLD FAMOUS TALE OF DRACULA.
THE END